PEBBLES FROM A BROKEN JAR
Fables and Hero Stories
from Old China

Retold by Frances Alexander

The Bobbs-Merrill Company, Inc.
Indianapolis
New York

The Bobbs-Merrill Company, Inc.
A Subsidiary of Howard W. Sams & Co., Inc.
Publishers   Indianapolis   Kansas City   New York

*Presented for the
pleasure of old and young and
dedicated to my sister,
Mary C. Alexander,
who spent thirty-six years
in China as missionary, teacher
and publisher.*

Foreword

A few decades ago a traveler in China could see villagers gathered under wayside trees listening to professional story tellers as they dramatized romantic legends, war heroism, and folk wisdom.

This was theater in its simplest form—a form that has passed on from generation to generation much of China's literary heritage. Many of the stories were long and involved dealing with war lords, moon maidens, or immortals on supernatural adventures. But some were brief fable-like stories for bringing wisdom to the young. Here are presented eighteen of these brief stories, chosen largely because they are brief, wise, and pleasing.

The twelve illustrations are from scissor cuts made by students in Cheefu, China, more than forty years ago. For centuries scissor cuts have been used to adorn greetings and ceremonial messages, and for decorating walls and window panes on festival occasions.

FRANCES ALEXANDER

Contents

Wu Meng, the Thoughtful
FOURTH CENTURY A.D.

Wu Meng loved his parents and it worried him that the mosquitoes bit them until they could hardly sleep at night.

The loving son decided to do something to save his parents from this trouble. He moved the rain barrel over a little further and made room for his own bedboard out on the porch. He went to bed early so that the mosquitoes could feast on him rather than on his mother and father.

How to Weigh an Elephant

THIRD CENTURY A.D.

A Chinese Emperor of the Wei Kingdom was presented an elephant by one of his subjects. He gave his ministers three days to tell him the weight of the elephant. If they could not tell him, they would lose their heads.

The ministers had only small scales. How could they weigh such a large creature? They worked hard to find the answer. By the third day they were sure they would lose their heads.

But Prince Chung, a young boy, declared that he could weigh the elephant. A great crowd gathered at the water's edge as the young prince had the elephant placed on a boat. The prince then swam around the boat marking the water line with red paint.

Then the elephant was removed and the boat filled with stones until it sank to the red water line. The boy weighed the stones one by one, added the weights together and found the weight of the elephant.

Thus Prince Chung saved the heads of the ministers and gained great favor with the Emperor of Wei.

The Polite Children

Two small children wandered into the woods. There they met a fierce tiger. Even in great fright they remembered their manners. They bowed politely, bumping their heads to the ground.

The tiger was surprised and amused, but he decided to be polite too. So he bowed and bumped his head to the ground. The children kept bowing and the tiger kept bowing until the villagers rushed out and drove the tiger away.

Tao K'an and His Mother

Tao K'an and his mother were poor, but they always tried to make visitors welcome and at ease. "Hospitality is a great virtue," said the mother.

One day during a snow storm a traveller came to their house for shelter. The mother slipped out to the market and sold her hair to buy food for the stranger.

Meantime Tao K'an cut up the straw mat on his bed board to feed the stranger's horse.

The guest proved to be an important magistrate from whom Tao K'an learned many things; and after that snow storm he had a friend at court to help him toward high office.

Wen Yen~Poh, the Thinker
SUNG DYNASTY (960-1280)

Wen Yen-Poh and some other children were playing with a large hollow ball when it bounced into a hollow tree. They worked hard with crooked sticks and straight ones but could not get the ball out.

Then Yen-Poh said: "Let's bring water from the spring and fill the hollow."

The children took turns carrying buckets of water and soon they had floated the ball up to where they could reach it.

Wen Yen-Poh later became a great minister of state.

Why Frogs Speak Chinese

An old man and his wife were walking over a bridge. The wife, while looking over the railing at the lotus blossoms, dropped her melon in the water. (*Gwa* is Chinese for *melon*.)

The husband, in trying to get the melon, dropped his staff in the water. (*Guer* is Chinese for *staff*.)

The husband reached for the staff and he fell in.

The wife reached for the husband and she fell in.

A good fairy in pity for the old ones changed them into frogs and now you can still hear them talking about their melon and staff: "Gwa-guer! Gwa-guer! Gwa-guer!"

Sze-Ma Gwang, the Quick One

SUNG DYNASTY (960-1280)

Sze-Ma Gwang was playing with some neighbor children when one of them fell headfirst into a large clay water jar and was about to drown.

The other children cried out for help; but Gwang threw a rock and broke a hole in the jar. The water poured out and the child was saved.

Gwang later became a great ruler.

Tsai Shun, the Faithful

FIRST CENTURY A.D.

Tsai Shun's mother had always been afraid in thunderstorms. When Shun saw a dark cloud gathering he stayed near the house; and when the storm began, he would take his mother's hand and say, "Do not be afraid, Mother; the storm will soon be over."

Even after his mother died if there was a thunderstorm Shun hurried to his mother's grave, knelt down beside it and said softly, "Sleep well, Mother; the storm will soon be over."

Wong Siang, the Clever

THIRD CENTURY A.D.

For many days Wong Siang's mother was too sick to eat anything. One day, however, she called Siang and said, "Now, son, at last I can eat. Bring me a fish."

The mother did not know that the river was frozen over solid.

What could Siang do? He went to the river, hung his clothes on a limb and lay down on the ice. After a time the heat of his body melted the ice and a fish popped out. He hurried to the house and cooked the fish. His mother ate it and soon she was well.

The Wise Judge

One morning a judge named Pao Ching rode through the market place and saw a boy crying by the roadside.

"Why are you crying?" asked Pao Ching.

"Your Honor," said the boy, rising and pointing to his empty basket, "I sold my fried fritters for two hundred cash. I put my basket on this stone while I rested, and now my money is gone."

"The stone is to blame," said the judge, and he ordered his men to bring the stone to court and beat it with bamboo sticks.

The crowd began to laugh.

"Quiet!" shouted the judge. "Each of you shall spend three days in jail for being impolite."

The people knelt, begging forgiveness.

"Very well, I will forgive you if each of you casts twenty cash into this bowl of water before me."

One by one they cast in their coins. When the third man threw his money in, a bit of grease floated on top of the water.

"There is the thief," said Pao Ching. "Search him!"

And in the pockets of this third man they found the stolen money. The court adjourned, the thief went to jail, and the boy took the fritter money home to his mother.

Kwang Heng, the Book Lover

FIRST CENTURY B.C.

Kwang Heng was a farmer boy. He had no money to go to school, but from his playmates he learned to read.

When he was twelve Kwang Heng went to work in the home of a man who had many books. "Do not pay me high wages, sir," he said, "but lend me your books to read at night."

"Surely you may borrow my books," said the scholar.

Because he had to help his parents buy rice, Kwang Heng could not buy candles for his night reading. A friend whose room joined Kwang Heng's room allowed him to cut a hole in the wall and read by his light.

Thus Kwang Heng became a man of great learning, was able to teach others, and help his country.

Mang Jen and His Mother

Mang Jen was hired by an overlord to guard the state fish ponds. One day when no one was looking he caught up a large net full of the state's best fish, dried them, and sent them as a gift to his mother.

The mother would not have the fish, but sent them back saying, "It is a great sorrow to me, Son, that you have killed the fish you were hired to take care of."

Lao Lai-Tse, the Tactful

SIXTH CENTURY B.C.

Lao Lai-Tse was seventy years old. His ninety year old father and mother sent word that they would come to visit him.

Lai-Tse was pleased. He had ducks and bamboo sprouts steamed to tenderness so that the old ones would not be reminded of their bad teeth. He opened for them a wide door where there were no high steps to remind them of their stiff knees.

When the parents came Lai-Tse was wearing a coat of many colors and sitting on the floor playing with his rattle so that the old ones would forget their years in thinking him still a child.

Chi and Yi

Chi and Yi, two friends, were walking in the woods when they met a bear.

Chi, the larger boy, climbed a tree and did not help his friend. Yi, who could not climb fast enough, dropped down as if he were dead.

The bear sniffed a long time at Yi's ear, then went on his way.

"What secret did he whisper in your ear?" called Chi from a high limb.

"He told me he had already had his dinner, but he advised me hereafter to have nothing to do with those who think only of themselves."

The Sage in the Cave

Fourth Century A.D.

The sage, Wang Shen, had two pupils, Sun Bin and Pang Djuen. He wanted to test them. "I am in this cave and neither of you can make me leave it," he said.

Bin, the younger, made the first try, "Come Teacher," he shouted. "Come quickly. Two dragons are fighting on the hill." But the sage stayed in the cave.

Then Djuen, the older, shouted, "Ah, here comes the high-ruler of the province. You must come out to receive him." But the sage did not move.

The two boys tried and tried, but the sage stayed on in the cave.

Finally, Bin sighed and said, "If I could only make you come out, I could make you go back in."

At this the sage came out. "Now make me go back in," he said.

"Let's not bother," said Bin. "I only wanted to get you out."

The Bird on the Roof

Yi was so pleased with his new wife that he sat on the porch talking to her instead of planting his rice. His spirit mother, fearing that her son would starve, changed herself into a bookoo bird and perched on the roof of her son's house. All day long she called in bird notes, "Boo koo! Boo koo!" which in Chinese means: "Plant your rice! Plant your rice!"

Yi finally understood and rushed out to plant his rice just in time to make a good crop..

But Yi still loved his wife and his home so much that every spring the bird mother had to sit on his roof top and call to him, "Boo koo! Boo koo!" (Plant your rice! Plant your rice!)

One Hundred Thousand Arrows

THIRD CENTURY A.D.

Chu-Ko Liang was ordered by his overlord to provide one hundred thousand arrows at once because the enemy was in the harbor ready to attack.

Chu-Ko Liang consulted the weather currents and knew that in three days there would be a heavy fog. He promised the overlord that in three days he would bring the one hundred thousand arrows.

Then Chu-Ko Liang had twenty boats launched, their decks filled with straw men. The fog settled down around them, trumpets and drums sounded, and the boats moved out toward the enemy.

The enemy, thinking they were being attacked, shot the straw men full of arrows—more than one hundred thousand of them. And thus Chu-Ko provided the arrows that saved his great city.

Fear, the Greatest Enemy

The Kingdom of Chu was attacked by the Army of Chi.

On a dark night the king of Chu sent one of his cleverest soldiers into the enemy camp, saying, "Bring me the general's tent."

When the general of Chi woke next morning, there was no tent over his head and no trace of it anywhere. But soon a messenger came from the king of Chu, bringing the tent and saying, "Last night my soldiers were gathering sticks and brought your tent with them by accident. My regrets!"

The next night the king said to his clever soldier, "Bring me the general's pillow." And the soldier did as he was told.

When the general woke there was no pillow under his head and he was alarmed. But soon the king of Chu returned the pillow by messenger, saying, "Last night my soldiers were gathering sticks and by accident brought home your pillow."

The next night the soldier found the general asleep in his uniform, and it took skill to slip off the medal the king of Chu had asked him to bring.

But when the general woke the next morning his medal was gone from his coat. After several hours there came a messenger from the king of Chu, saying, "The king of Chu asks your pardon. His unworthy soldiers were gathering sticks and by chance brought home your precious medal. He sends it back with regrets."

Now the general of Chi was really frightened. "The next thing, they will be stealing my head," he said. And he ordered his army to go home.